THE ADVE
MR LIGHTHOUSE MAN
AND THE
INGENIOUS MICE

Printed in Great Britain by
Biddles Books Limited, King's Lynn, Norfolk

This book is dedicated
to my wife, who is a
wonderwoman

CONTENTS

CHAPTER 1
The Amazing Beginning

This lighthouse is the last one to have a person looking after it, and I am the last lighthouse man living in a lighthouse twenty-four hours a day. The lighthouse is very tall and, over the years, has been painted in many different colours and, importantly, has a very bright light right at the top. It is built on a remote piece of land in this wonderful country of ours, looking out over a great and dangerous stretch of river and seaway. My lighthouse light shines very brightly, helping to make the navigation of ships as safe as possible along this treacherous coastal area.

Officially, I am told, all written information reads that this lighthouse is automatic, but I am here to operate it, so it isn't, if you see what I mean. For some reason, the technical people in the depot situated far away inland cannot make the light come on and go off automatically at the correct time, which is what should happen, but doesn't happen. I have to be here to switch the light on at night and switch it off during the day. The light at night makes sure all the ships and other craft be aware of these treacherous cliffs and stop them from crashing into these dangerous, rocky shores.

At the correct time this evening, I switched the lighthouse light on and sat peacefully dozing in my armchair when suddenly, without any warning, an alarm sounded and I woke up to find all the lights out, including the lighthouse light, which isn't a good thing at all for a lighthouse.

I sat for a moment wondering what had happened, then saw it was a very serious situation indeed, and sprang up out of my chair, went into the switch room and pushed the button for the emergency electrical generator to start. Fortunately, it started, and produced temporary electricity and, delightfully, the lighthouse light came on again. It also gave me two emergency lights inside the lighthouse, so I could see what I was doing and where I was going, thankfully.

A few thoughts struck me. One - I have never seen the lighthouse light fail before and, two - the emergency generator has now temporarily restored the electrical power to enable the lighthouse light to shine, which was a really good thing indeed.

My inquisitive wondering settled on why the electricity had failed in the first place, and I walked over to the wall where the very old electrical fuse box was situated. As I gently studied it, I noticed, out of the corner of my eye, something move and, to my surprise and bewilderment, I saw a mouse. Not an ordinary mouse, but a handsome, upright, very smart, grey mouse, with fine whiskers and fairly large ears. This mouse was a lot larger than an ordinary mouse and was, amazingly, dressed in a blue waistcoat, black-and-white striped breeches, red socks and blue trainers. It also had what looked like a watch strapped to its wrist. I was so stunned I couldn't say anything, only stand and stare. Suddenly, this extraordinary creature spoke to me, which surprised me even further; I blinked my eyes in astonishment and scratched the back of my head.

In a very proud-sounding voice the mouse said, "The lighthouse light went out."

"Yes," I stammered, and I wrinkled my brow. On one hand, I was wondering why the electricity had failed and, on the other hand, I was wondering where this elegant-ly-dressed mouse had come from, and how it was possible that this mouse was talking to me.

The same voice spoke again. "It went very dark."

"Yes," I said.

This colourfully-dressed mouse then raised itself on its hind legs, which made it even bigger and, with a fairly serious facial expression, made a statement. "I think we've had a malfunction of the light."

"Yes, it looks like it," I proclaimed, in a surprisingly calm voice.

The mouse then asked, "If you want me to, I could get Brian the Explorer mouse to come and investigate?"

I was still in a kind of daze, and could only blurt out, "Hang on a second; who are you?"

It maintained its composure, stood to attention, folded its arms across its chest, and lifted its head.

"Ah yes; I'm George, and I'm a lighthouse mouse; in fact, I am Head of all the lighthouse mouse."

Still slightly thunderstruck, I retorted, "Oh, are you?! Well, hello George, head of all the lighthouse mice, nice to meet you. Who's Brian the Explorer mouse?" I paused after saying all this, scratched my head again, and slowly changed my feelings about the situation, also, I changed my tone of voice, making it a little gentler, and asked, "Do you think Brian the Explorer could help?"

"Yes," he replied, "I think he could."

I'd only just met this head mouse and didn't know anything about him, or anything about the other mice; plus, I hadn't a clue what to do so, amazingly, I just said, "Well, can you get him?"

Then, after I said it, I thought, "Why have I said that? I'm asking one mouse to fetch another mouse."

George the Head mouse looked at me and said, "Can you unscrew the fuse box cover, and I will get him? Oh, and by the way, the lighthouse mouse are always called 'mouse', not 'mice'."

My mind noted I must always say 'mouse'. I then went to the fuse box and pushed the main isolator switch upwards to the 'off' position, which was essential before carrying out any work with electricity and, with my screwdriver, opened the fuse box cover. I found both fuses had blown and, therefore, the electrical connection was broken. By the time I had done all this, another mouse had arrived and introduced himself.

"Hello, I'm Brian the Explorer."

This fellow was the same size as George, but thinner, and was dressed in a bright-blue all-in-one overall with a white stripe across the front, and a watch, or whatever, strapped to his wrist and a sort of plastic hat on his head.

He asked, "Can you lift me, please, and put me in the upper side of the fuse box?"

For some unknown, extraordinary reason, I bent down and held out my hand, and he immediately jumped onto it. I found he was surprisingly light. I lifted him and put him where he requested. He said, "Thank you," and disappeared up inside the electrical cable tube of the fuse box.

Within only about a minute, George the Head mouse spoke up again. "He has found the problem and has arranged for Marilyn and the team to come with a new cable."

At this point, there were far too many questions I wanted to ask. How did he know what Brian had found? Who were

Marilyn and the team? In the end I just blurted out, "Err, Marilyn?"

"Yes, she's the backbone of the team."

I decided not to enquire any further about the team or Marilyn and, with wonderment, watched as a troop of mouse appeared, all dressed in very smart, brightly-coloured striped breeches, waistcoats, socks and trainers, each of them in the same colours. They were spectacular, and arrived with what looked like an electrical repair kit.

Marilyn, who was pretty, and wearing pink-and-white striped breeches, said, "Hello; can you hand this up to Brian?"

I took it from her and lifted it up to the fuse box. A little hand came out from the upper cable tube, took it from me, said, "Thank you," then disappeared.

We all waited and, within a minute or two, Brian the Explorer reappeared and requested me to help him back to the floor. I did what he asked, and again he said, "Thank you," then he said, "It's all fixed; you can put the lighthouse light back on now."

With that, all the mouse waved and shouted, "See you later," and they were gone.

I stood, slightly dazed and perplexed but, outwardly, I managed a satisfyingly pleasing smile.

Slowly and thoughtfully, I replaced the fuses with new ones and screwed the fuse box cover back on. I stopped the generator and pulled the fuse-box isolating switch down to the 'on' position, and the lights and the main lighthouse light came on immediately.

"Jolly good," I whispered, and my pleasing smile broadened.

CHAPTER 2
George Head Mouse

After what had happened with the lighthouse lights, and Brian the Explorer, and the rest of the mouse, I finally slept surprisingly well.

Early next morning, I turned off the lighthouse light and busied myself by carrying out my daily routine maintenance. I also spent a lot of time thinking and trying to reason what had happened the previous night. I kept musing over and over in my brain, whether it was real, or whether I had dreamt about the mouse, and the light going off, and Brian the Explorer coming and putting it back on again. Eventually, I came to the amazing conclusion it was all incredibly real.

On completion of my thoughts and a bacon sandwich, I sat at my kitchen table cradling a nice hot mug of tea and, from somewhere, a very proud voice said, "Mr Lighthouse man."

I looked around and saw George the Head mouse sitting by the leg of my table, dressed as smartly as he was last night only, this morning, he was wearing a different pair of very fancy trainers. I was still perplexed at his sudden arrival but, somehow, I knew I had to get used to it.

"Can I come up?" he asked.

"Yes," I said, and he scrambled up onto the tabletop, sat on his hind legs facing me, wrinkled his brow, and spoke.

"Brian the Explorer did a really good job last night, finding and repairing the lighthouse light's electrical cable."

"Yes," I said, "can you please thank him for me? I can see why he is called Brian the Explorer."

"Yes, I will thank him, but I have come to see you this morning because I have a minor problem of my own, and I am hoping you could possibly help me?"

I was a little taken aback by this sudden request, but managed to reply, "If I can help you, I will."

George rather shyly began speaking, "Brian the Explorer wants to try and return to Mouseland and I've got to make a speech before he goes. I'm not very good at making speeches, and it's not going to be easy for me. It is the first time for a very long time any mouse has tried to go back to Mouseland, and every mouse will be hoping he makes the journey safely. We will all be very happy if he gets there but, on the other hand, very sorry to see him go. He is the Explorer mouse, and he thinks that, with all the work he has put in, he has a good chance of making it to Mouseland. To us, he is a very special mouse."

In the first place, I was astounded that George the Head mouse had accepted me so easily, and puzzled over it for a second; then I thought the best thing to do was for me to accept him. So, I didn't ask any questions about Mouseland, or anything else, and just accepted him and replied, "I understand; how can I help?"

"Well," said George, "it will help if I could go through my speech with you, if that's all right."

I settled back in my chair and indicated for him to begin.

"Oh, right," he said. "This is what I am going to say in my speech," and he began. "Brian is our Explorer mouse and has been here since the beginning. He is very good at exploring although, occasionally, he takes things too far and sometimes stretches things to the limit. For example, the time he made those gadgets for his feet, so he could climb up panes of glass; it nearly caused him to fall and break his neck. But that is why we love him, and why he is such a good Explorer mouse."

George looked at me. I raised my eyebrows and smiled; he steadied himself and then continued with his speech. "Brian has always done his best for us, for he is one of us. He loves us all, and we love him dearly in return. We could not wish for a better explorer and, when he goes, he will be missed more than anyone can say."

At this point, tears flowed down his little cheeks, past his nose, and fell in large droplets onto the table. He looked at me as if to say, "What a softy I am." I put my hand out to console him.

He appreciated it, recovered himself, did his best to smile, and then went on, "This is more of my speech... We will all miss him when he goes, but he really wants to do this because he is the best Explorer mouse, and he will be the first mouse to go back to Mouseland."

He stopped speaking, and then explained, "I know I will cry when I make the speech. If I do, all the other mouse won't say, 'Pull yourself together, what are you, a man or a mouse?' They won't say that, will they?"

I smiled in a big way. "No, they won't say that."

"Do you think my speech is a good one?"

"Yes, I think it is a very fine speech indeed."

"Thank you, Mr Lighthouse man, for listening," and he scurried down the table leg, shouted "bye-bye" and was off.

I thought to myself, "I don't think I am ever going to be lonely again."

CHAPTER 3
The Memento

While sitting in my armchair, reading my book, a deep but gentle voice suddenly spoke to me.

"Mr Lighthouse man."

I looked down and there, at my feet, dressed in a brown waistcoat, black-and-white breeches, brown socks and bright-blue trainers, was a rather strong, good-looking, muscular mouse. He was sitting up on his hind legs, holding a stick. To me, it was a stick, but I suggest that, to him, it was a long, round piece of wood. He also had something strapped on his wrist.

On seeing him, I was pleasantly surprised by my calm mental attitude, and impressed by my ability at getting used to seeing these mouse suddenly appearing and disappearing.

I smiled. "Have you broken your stick?"

"In a way," he said, then announced himself. "I am the Engineer mouse; normally, I would send my assistant for things like this, but it is about time I met you. I am Big Sam."

"Well, it is nice to meet you, Big Sam. What is your assistant called, Little Sam?"

"No."

"Well, Small Sam?"

"No."

"What then?"

"Mabel."

"Oh, she's a girl mouse."

"Yes."

"Oh, right; well, what can I do for you?"

"A long time ago, Brian the Explorer always had a spade he used for exploring; then, one day, he accidentally broke the handle and, since then, he has never used it. To him, it was an old favourite friend, if you see what I mean. He had it for about fifty warm-colds and, one day, he broke it digging and never fixed it. He always meant to repair it, but he never got around to it. If we mend the spade, he can take it with him to Mouseland as a reminder of his time here at the lighthouse. It will be a memento of all the warm-colds he spent here. We intend to write on the handle of the spade 'The Life of Brian'."

I understood what he was saying and asked, "Can I have a look at it?" Before I had finished speaking, he had climbed up onto the arm of my chair, carrying the old spade-handle.

He handed it to me and said, "It is made of wood and, if we start to make a new handle, he might see us making it, and it will spoil the surprise. It would be great if you could help us by making a new handle."

After looking at it, I discovered it wasn't a stick at all, but a nice, round, well-fashioned piece of wood with the end broken off. To me, it was very similar to the wooden stakes I used to support the flowers in my pot plants. I rose from my chair, went to the window-sill, withdrew one of the many plant support stakes from one of the pots, cleaned it, gauged it against the broken spade handle, and found the diameter to be only ever so slightly larger than the handle.

Big Sam watched everything with keen interest.

I asked. "Do you want me to cut it to the right length?" His eyes opened wide, and he gave me a nod and an agreeable smile.

"Can you cut it to three elbow-arms long?" and he put his arm along the wooden plant support three times. "Can you cut it there, please?" he said.

I went through to my workbench in the other room, cut it to length, returned to my chair, gave it back to him and asked, "By the way, what is a 'warm-cold'?"

"It is the time it takes all of us to go all the way around the sun."

I whispered to myself, "Ah, yes, I see; a year."

He looked pleased, then put the wooden spade handle over his shoulder, winked at me, ran down the chair, turned and said, "Thank you very much, Mr Lighthouse man. H.M.G. will be pleased."

I queried, "H.M.G. is not, 'His Majesty George,' is it?"

As he ran off, I heard him laughing, or rather chuckling, "Ha, ha, ha, 'His Majesty George' indeed, ho, ho, ho."

I smiled; ah yes, my mistake, it must be, 'Head mouse George,' then wondered whether the stick was the real reason he came to see me, or was it something else? I had a lot to learn about these mouse.

CHAPTER 4
Discovering the Past

Sitting in my armchair contemplating my new situation, I found my general feeling to be one of utmost delight, and came to the firm conclusion I was more than fond of all these extraordinary, remarkable lighthouse mouse. It was the way they conducted themselves, and their polite, charming behaviour. They lived here on this piece of land, contentedly, in a world all of their own, and they seemed to be self-contained, a position I myself greatly admire.

When I first met George, Head Lighthouse mouse, he sat on his hind legs and used his front paws as arms, then spread his little hands out in a kindly gesture. By doing this, he gave me a sort of calmness and influenced me not to be startled or surprised when he spoke. He always said "mouse" even when he meant mice, and it was the look in his eyes that influenced me to do the same. He liked it when I said "mouse", so I kept saying it; now I can't stop.

Sitting here thinking about what has happened over the past few days is fascinating, and very interesting indeed, but there are two things, in particular, I find ever so slightly more intriguing than any others. How was it these lighthouse mouse suddenly appeared from seemingly nowhere? Also, where did they come from?

I have been in charge of the lighthouse for more years than I care to remember and have always been by myself.

What was it that triggered all these delightful little creatures to arrive out of the blue? Even more so, how was I going to discover what had happened in the past years? For the past thirty-odd years, I have never seen any sign of any ordinary mouse, and there has definitely never been any sign of any lighthouse mouse. Then, from nowhere, when the lighthouse light went out, they suddenly appeared. On reflection, I didn't mind these lovely mouse to be here - it is quite nice to have some friendly company. Now, sitting here in my armchair, I can't help thinking about the complete mystery of it all. I suppose the easiest way to find out would be to ask George, but I was disinclined to venture down this path, because I had already asked him why I hadn't met him before, and he answered by saying, "You weren't around the last time the lighthouse light went out. It was a long time ago."

He didn't want to give me any more information, and it was quite deliberate. To pursue it further would be churlish and, possibly, rude, so I decided that discovering what happened in the past was best left alone.

All this extraordinary, present company around me brought amusement and pleasure into my life, and that was good enough for me. No! Discovering what happened when the lighthouse light went out is going to remain a mystery.

Maybe the mystery will resolve itself in the end.

CHAPTER 5
Big Sam

After my contemplations, I rose from my armchair and carried out further daily duties. It is essential now more than ever to keep this lighthouse in tip-top condition. When it is dark, my light shines brightly; even when it is a little foggy, my light shines through to warn the captains of the passing ships about the presence of this remote piece of land. Ships from all over the world pass along this stretch of water, and it is imperative they are warned of the danger of crashing onto these rocks and the dreadful possibility of loss of life.

This thought always spurs me on to carry out my duties with great care and thoroughness.

As I was sitting in my armchair going through my checklist, a voice below me said, "It's me again."

I looked down, and sitting on the floor was Big Sam, the Engineer mouse; I recognised him because of his muscular frame. He was still wearing his waistcoat, breeches, socks and trainers, but the difference today was mainly due to the fact that he was wearing a very smart, white, flat cap.

"Hello, Big Sam," I said, "I like your flat cap."

"Thanks," was his reply, and he smiled. "I've come to ask you a question."

I waited for a moment, but could not prevent a large smile appearing on my face, and it momentarily stopped me from answering. He knew why I had this enormous grin, and began smiling himself. This little fellow in front of me was so comical in his white cap, but what made it even funnier, the cap was placed at a slightly jaunty angle. His smile, like my smile, eventually developed into an enormous grin.

He looked up at me, blinked and, with a twinkle in his eye, suggested, "Would it be any better if I took my cap off? Although I'm not really allowed to remove it yet."

"No, no, keep your cap on," I mumbled, half chuckling. "Tell me, what is your question?"

"Well, the spade handle turned out to be just right. Marilyn and the team have inspected it and said it is exactly like the old spade. Brian the Explorer will love it."

Then he added, "We are Lighthouse mouse, and we like the odd surprise. Brian the Explorer doesn't know we have repaired his spade and we think, if he takes the spade with him to Mouseland as a memento, it will be terrific."

I thought to myself, "Why a spade?" Surely there were other things he could take? Maybe it was a very famous spade and, long ago on his exploring, he and it had discovered things of extraordinary importance. It was another of those mysteries.

Big Sam wasn't finished. "Another reason I came to see you is for you to accept this," and he gestured to his right. Along the floor walked Marilyn and the colourfully-dressed team, carrying what looked like a mouse carved out of a piece of oak. It was very nearly the same size as they were.

He continued, "This mouse is a message mouse. If you want to see any of us, just leave a message. We will always know you have left one. Also, we will be able to put messages on it for you to read."

Marilyn and the team stepped forward for me to receive it. I bent down and lifted it out of their hands. It wasn't as heavy as I anticipated, indicating it wasn't made of wood at all, but some other material. From its looks, it was impossible to tell it wasn't oak. The whole thing was a statue of a lighthouse mouse sitting, on hind legs, with its hands out, as if waiting to give or receive something. It was indeed a very beautiful object. I was slightly taken aback by this lovely mouse and stumbled for words, and eventually said, "This is very beautiful; thank you very much, I will treasure it and use it as often as possible."

Everyone smiled huge smiles, then Marilyn and the team scampered across the floor and were gone.

Big Sam waved them off and turned to me. "The second reason I came was to invite you to join us and watch Brian the Explorer's departure to Mouseland." He said this with his eyes wide open, hoping I would say yes.

I thought it was a great idea, so replied, "Yes, I will be delighted to come."

"OK; someone will arrive later and show you the way. Oh, you must wear a hat, because everyone will be wearing a hat."

I thought, "Wait a minute, I am having a struggle keeping my laughter at bay because of Big Sam's cap. If all the mouse, at the departure of Brian the Explorer, are wearing a hat and they are anything like Big Sam's hat, how am I going to stop myself from laughing?" I was about to ask the question, but it was too late; he doffed his cap and was gone.

"Oh, heck," I whispered to myself.

CHAPTER 6
The Professor

After the swift departure of Big Sam, I was left not knowing what time, or even what day, Brian the Explorer was leaving to try to go to Mouseland. My next thought was what hat to wear. The choice was not difficult, because I had only two.

I opened the cupboard door, took the bright-yellow, broad-brimmed sou'wester hat usually used when it rained, and put it on my head, and immediately decided it was not the right one to see Brian the Explorer go to Mouseland. Fortunately, a long time ago, someone bought me a fedora hat for men. I put this on my head and went to the mirror, looked at myself, wrinkled my brow, and thought, "Well, it doesn't suit me, but it has to be the one for the departure of Brian the Explorer."

As I was studying myself one more time, I heard a voice say, "I think that's better than the sou'wester."

I looked down and saw a heavily-whiskered older mouse. He was quite noticeably older than the others, because he was sitting on his hind legs not as upright as the other mouse, and his large whiskers and eyebrows were a lighter grey colour. He was wearing glasses and dressed more soberly, although his breeches, socks and trainers were in bright colours.

I sat down in my chair. "Oh, hello; I like your trainers and your socks."

He looked at me, gave me a big smile and then paused, with his eyes wandering about as if to say, "They are a bit bright, aren't they?"

He then asked, "Can I come and sit on the arm of your chair?"

I indicated for him to come up. At first, he managed to climb quite easily but, as he advanced further, he began to slow. I didn't know whether or not to give him a hand, finally deciding it best to leave him alone to avoid the possibility of hurting his pride.

He arrived slightly out of breath and needed a minute to recover. I watched him puff out his little cheeks a couple of times.

Eventually, he focused his attention on me. "I am Professor Universe, and I am the psychologist for all the lighthouse mouse."

We then had an extended hesitation until he finally said, "I can be your psychologist if you want me to be."

Crikey, these mouse did make me smile. What an offer! I could only think of saying, "That would be very nice."

My response cheered him, and immediately, his eyes brightened. "Oh, right," he said, and sat up a little straighter.

"Now, you are aware Brian the Explorer is going back to Mouseland. I know you didn't know him very well, but you may still miss him when he goes. I have come to help you get over any problems you may have of missing him after he has gone. We must all learn to face things without him, and the best way to do this is to think of him, breathe in deeply, wait, then breathe out and sigh, like this." He remained silent, presumably thinking of Brian the Explorer, then he breathed in, waited, then breathed out with a quite loud sigh, and it made him smile.

"Can you do that?"

He was right of course; I didn't know Brian very well, but he was a nice, polite mouse, and really helpful when the lighthouse light went out. I thought it may be a good idea to do what the professor asked.

"Yes, I can do that."

"Right," he said, "let's try and practise it together. First, think of Brian the Explorer, then breathe in, wait, then breathe out and sigh. Are you ready?"

"Yes," I said.

"Right, now think of Brian the Explorer."

I instantly thought of Brian the Explorer... and breathed in very deeply and waited.... He then said, "Now breathe out and sigh." I then breathed out and made a noise as I sighed; and he was right, I did feel good, and said, "I really do feel better now about Brian leaving."

He smiled. "Then my visit has been worthwhile. Oh, and by the way, Brian's departure is at twenty-two hours; that's ten o'clock tomorrow night. Someone will come for you." He then went backwards, not forwards, down the chair, waved, and was gone.

I thought to myself, "I'll try that again." I thought of Brian the Explorer, took a deep breath, waited, breathed out, then sighed, and yes, it did feel good.

I had no problems with the light during the night and, in the morning, after checking everything, I sat down in my chair to think.

CHAPTER 7
Ronnie-Odd-Socks

On top of my writing desk, I noticed an envelope in the arms of my new, beautiful message-mouse. I walked over and took the divine object in my hands, and gently slipped the small envelope from its grasp, then placed it back into its original position.

On returning to my chair, I gingerly opened the envelope and took out my first ever message.

It read, 'Ronnie-Odd-Socks will visit you this morning at about eleven hours. Thank you.'

That's all it said. The whole thing brought a smile to my face, wondering who Ronnie-Odd-Socks was and if he indeed wore odd socks.

After carrying out my duties in the lighthouse, I sat comfortably in my chair with my book and waited for eleven o'clock.

At precisely that time, a voice said, "Hello, Mr Lighthouse man, I'm Ronnie-Odd-Socks."

I looked down and saw a very handsome, tall mouse with smooth skin, quite large ears and gentle eyes. He was dressed like all the other mouse, only he wore odd socks. His voice was that of a young mouse.

"Oh, hello Ronnie-Odd-Socks, I like your socks and your trainers."

"Thanks," he said, "I try my best."

Moving my hand in an encouraging way, I invited him to come and sit on the arm of my chair. He received my invitation, deftly climbed up and arrived in double-quick time and sat on his hind legs. He waited, possibly a little nervous, or maybe not knowing where to start, so to encourage him, I gently said, "It's nice to see you."

I was pleased to see he had overcome his nervousness. "I'm the technical mouse, and work with, and understand, all the tiny microchips and technical data and all the other things to do with electronics."

I listened, and then asked, "How can I help you, Ronnie-Odd-Socks?"

He sat, pondering in thought for a moment. Slowly, he gathered himself together and said, "A light will shine at midnight tonight for one minute, from the stretch of water where the mouth of this big river meets the sea, and I would like you to partially cover the lighthouse light for one minute and stop the lighthouse light from shining at the exact position of the light."

He waited, looked directly at me, then continued, "I know this is highly irregular, but it will help all the lighthouse mouse a great deal."

He was right, of course; to do this would be highly irregular, but he said it would be for only a minute. Fortunately, this lighthouse had a black blind fitted, enabling the light to be shut off in any position around the light. I momentarily wondered how the lighthouse mouse knew about this blind, and the possibility it could be drawn across a section of the light. I dismissed the thought for a later day and asked, "How much of the light do you want me to cover?"

He replied, "Oh, only a small amount; only about sixty degrees, which is not a lot."

I thought about it long and hard. "About sixty degrees, you say, at the light shining from where the river meets the sea?" I contemplated it for a moment. "Is there anything else?"

"Yes," he said, "I want to be with you on the light platform at that time. If you do this for us, it will really help the lighthouse mouse."

I smiled, and looked at him sitting beside me in his trainers and odd socks. I couldn't help thinking, "I must do this for the lighthouse mouse." So I joyfully replied, "Yes, I will help you, and yes, you can come up onto the light platform with me."

The smile on the face of Ronnie-Odd-Socks beamed as bright as the lighthouse light.

"Right, thank you," he said, and shot off shouting, "See you before midnight."

CHAPTER 8
Lucinda Lids

After carrying out my normal duties, I ventured into the garden and continued working on my vegetable plot. It isn't an extremely large plot, but big enough to serve me well with consumables all year round. Whenever I have the time, I saunter across and dig, cut and tidy the plot, and get a great delight in planting and watching how the produce comes to life. I am very pleasantly surprised by how quickly things grow in this particular part of the garden.

Towards the shed at the back of the garden, I have cultivated an area where perennial flowers gather, and fruit trees blossom. This area, astonishingly, seems to flourish exceedingly well every year, with very little attention.

As darkness began to fall, I put my lighthouse light on, and was sitting in my armchair reading my book when a lighthouse mouse appeared. I figured this to be a lady mouse, for she wore pink trainers with white socks and, possibly normal for a lady mouse, pink-and-white vertical-striped breeches terminating just above the knee. She also wore a sky-blue waistcoat and an extraordinary, pale-blue, wide-brimmed hat. I was now getting quite used to these appearances and, therefore, was only a little surprised by her sudden arrival.

"Hello," she said, "I'm Lucinda Lids."

"Hello," I replied, "I like your hat."

She gave a little curtsy. "Thank you. Can I come and sit on the arm of your chair?"

I moved my hand and raised my eyebrows, indicating it was a good idea. Within a second she had climbed the chair and was sitting on her hind legs next to me.

"I like your name; is there a reason you are called Lucinda Lids?" She looked directly at me and fluttered her long, black eyelashes.

"Ah, yes, I see now," and I smiled.

She smiled back at me and spoke. "I am your guide. I've come to ask you to go to what we call the folly, situated on the outer boundary of the garden, and to invite you to the open-air gathering-place, built right at the back of the folly. This is where all the lighthouse mouse will tonight be assembling, for the departure of Brian the Explorer."

By using the word folly, I think she meant the old, stone-built empty structure, resembling a very large stone igloo; and she was right, it was positioned away to the far end of the garden. Many years ago, the folly, as she called it, had been built using local stone found in and around the region. It did remotely resemble a folly, as the stones were cemented in place and smoothed over. It gave the shape of a dome. It did look, I suppose, a bit foolish. The reason it was built is unclear; it originally had a door, now, unfortunately stoned up, making it impossible for anyone to enter inside. I cannot remember the last time I ventured over to it.

Lucinda Lids moved her arms in a flowing gesture, like a ballerina, indicating she should leave. As I rose from the armchair, she scampered down the side, turned, and said, "Oh, don't forget; when you come to the folly, you must wear your hat."

I took my hat and placed it on my head.

"Very nice," she said, fluttering her eyelashes, "I like that; see you in five minutes," and she was off.

With my hat on my head, I went out the lighthouse door and walked across the garden, then turned right at the vegetable plot, walked through the long grass, and made my way to the back of what she called the folly, which was lit in the same way as a theatre ghost light.

On my arrival, I saw Lucinda Lids waiting under the veranda, sitting on the top of the old stone table.

"Come and sit on one of the chairs," she said, and I sat down on one of the old wooden chairs beside the table. She walked across the tabletop and sat beside me. At that moment, a multitude of hats walked around from either side of the folly and assembled on the floor in front of us. Every hat was present: flat caps, baseball caps, flowered hats, and even a Kentucky Derby, all of different colours. I smiled, trying hard to keep it to just a smile.

The hats took their places and waited.

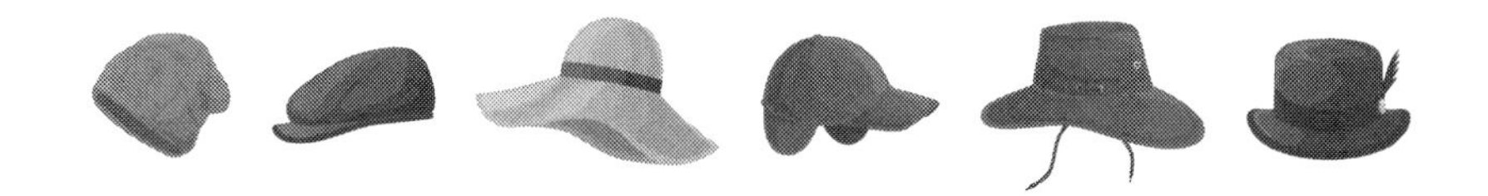

CHAPTER 9
Brian the Explorer

From my sitting position on the chair next to the table, I could nicely see, in the ghost light, all the assembled mouse in front of me, wearing striped breeches, blue waistcoats, and hats of many different shapes and colours. Brian the Explorer was positioned right in the centre of all the mouse, wearing his overall and with his helmet firmly on his head. He was standing very upright, with his spade fastened tightly onto his backpack and holding what looked like a round, reflecting device in each of his hands.

The full moon moved slowly across the sky, and everything went very quiet.

George the Head mouse stepped forward, moved his hands apart, and all mouse assembled did the same; then they all clapped three times together in unison and chorused, "Yes!"

The whole area echoed with the sound. This outburst took me a little by surprise and I thought it must be something they did on special occasions. My smile developed into a broad grin.

George made his speech, and cried like he said he would. Many mouse, like myself, became wrapped up in the occasion and struggled to hold back a tear.

On completion of his speech, George the Head mouse introduced Professor Universe. When he stepped forward, everyone assembled again, moved their hands apart, clapped three times in unison, and chorused, "Yes!"

The moon moved further across the sky, and the full light fell directly on to Brian the Explorer. Professor Universe steadied himself, then gestured to him as if to say, "Are you ready?"

Brian the Explorer put his arms forward and pressed the switches in his hands, and a light on his backpack flashed with astonishing brightness.

Professor Universe gave instructions. "Let us all think of 'Brian the Explorer'." I didn't mean to but, when thinking of Brian, I closed my eyes. I heard the Professor say, "Breathe in, wait, now breathe out, and sigh." Everyone sighed, and it was quite loud.

When I opened my eyes, I automatically looked over to where Brian was, but he was now no longer there, and the light from the moon had passed. All the mouse started to chat together. I didn't understand what they were saying, it seemed to be a different language. It was another of those mysteries. Would I ever find out what all these mysteries were about?

As the hats began to make their way around the side and back into the folly, Lucinda Lids looked at me. "There; the sigh was a good one. I am sure he will make it to Mouseland, and we all feel a lot better."

The strangest thing of all, she was right. I automatically did feel a lot better; I didn't miss Brian at all, although I knew he had gone.

Lucinda Lids looked at me. "Don't forget Ronnie-Odd-Socks will meet you in the lighthouse just before midnight," and she walked across the tabletop, turned, fluttered her eyelashes, and said, "Goodnight, Mr Lighthouse man," then slid down the table leg and was gone.

I made my way back to the lighthouse, checked everything was all right, made a cup of tea, and sat in my armchair to think about things. The moon definitely played a part in the happening, and the sighing was really good; it sort of made everything right.

My thoughts were interrupted by the sudden arrival of Ronnie-Odd-Socks. He stood in front of me in his brightly-coloured trainers, odd socks, black-and-white striped breeches, navy-blue waistcoat and a baseball cap.

"Hello," he said, "are you ready to go up to the lighthouse light platform?"

"Yes, I'm ready. How are you going to get up all those steps?"

He replied, "Don't worry about me," and he was off.

When I arrived at the platform, the light from the lighthouse was shining brightly and, amazingly, Ronnie-Odd-Socks was there to greet me.

He sat back on his hind legs, reached his full height and looked directly at me. "You are doing this for all the lighthouse mouse. Are you ready?"

"Yes," I said.

He stared directly at me; "Please keep looking at me all the time during this operation. When I raise my arm, please draw the blind across sixty degrees of the light to stop it shining on the position where the river meets the sea. We will then wait for a moment or two and, when I lower my arm, will you please open the blind and allow the light to shine on to the sea again?"

In a very excited manner, I replied, "Yes, I will do exactly as you say."

It was now very close to midnight.

CHAPTER 10
At the Midnight Hour

As midnight approached, the excitement in me increased every second, and my heartbeat quickened. My eyes were glued onto Ronnie-Odd-Socks, who had his head turned toward the river. I watched with keen anticipation and saw him raise his arm and, without any hesitation, I closed the blind and blocked the light from shining onto the river where it met the sea. Then, with my eyes constantly fixed on Ronnie-Odd-Socks, I waited for him to give me the signal to open the blind. Suddenly, without warning, there was a very bright flash of light, and he brought his arm down quickly. I nearly missed him doing it, and it made me fumble for a second. Eventually, I managed to open the blind, and the light from the lighthouse shone with a very bright light indeed onto the river where it met the sea, and everything returned to normal.

All this concentration and excitement exhausted me and forced me to lower my head, breathe in heavily, and puff out my cheeks as I breathed out.

Ronnie-Odd-Socks turned to me; I barely heard him whisper, ever so quietly, "We've done it."

I was not exactly sure what we had done but, whatever it was we were supposed to have done, we had done it.

Suddenly, another voice said, "Hello, I'm Horatio Science mouse."

I was so startled, it made me open my eyes wide and move my head backwards in complete surprise. I looked at Ronnie-Odd-Socks; he rolled his eyes and put his finger to his lips as if to say, "Keep this all a secret." I had seen many different things over the last weeks or so, but this was the most extraordinary.

They both stood looking at me, with their legs apart and their hands on their hips, and their faces full of satisfaction and euphoria. My face must have been a picture, because they started to laugh. I was completely astounded and began laughing myself, and put my hands on my hips to imitate them; it made them laugh even more, and point at me.

When everything settled down, I possibly should have asked where Horatio Science mouse had come from, but I didn't. They knew it would remain a secret with me although, in a quiet moment later, I possibly, might have a think about it.

Horatio Science was a very young, handsome mouse, with large eyes, and dressed in a style similar to all the other mouse, only he had horizontal-striped breeches, and a rucksack on his back.

Ronnie-Odd-Socks gestured to me and inquired, "Shall we go down to your armchair?"

I agreed, and descended the steps. On arrival in my room, I sat in my chair, and both mouse appeared and ran up onto the arms. I had Ronnie-Odd-Socks on the left and Horatio on the right.

They settled back on hind legs then, in unison, they both held out their arms, clapped their hands three times, then chorused, "Yes!"

What else could I do other than smile a broad smile?

They thanked me profusely for helping, then Horatio Science reached into his rucksack and pulled out a card with writing on it, and gave it to me. I couldn't make out the words, because the card was very small. He put his finger to his lips, and the card grew in size so I could make out the words; it read:

'Wish you were here Mr Lighthouse man, so I could thank you for seeing me off to Mouseland.' It was signed 'Brian the Explorer.' He had travelled back to Mouseland without using the lighthouse light and survived. I was absolutely delighted, and showed it in the expression on my face.

The two boys watched me, smiled, said they had things to do, ran down the arm of the chair, and were gone.

CHAPTER 11
A Message

The following morning, I noticed a folded piece of paper in my message mouse. It read, 'George the Head mouse will visit at fourteen hours.'

Between two and three o'clock in the afternoon is always a nice time for me, because it is when I finish my lighthouse duties, sit in my armchair and relax. The important thing I had to do today was to telephone Barry at the depot, to come in his big lorry with all my essential stores and other equipment. He was due tomorrow, and I needed to make sure of his arrival time and go over the list of things I had previously given him. It was important, because he would not be coming again for quite a while, and there were one or two things in addition that I wanted him to bring, and I was hoping he would include them. His lorry has a crane attached, enabling him to take away all my old, empty containers and replace them with new, full ones.

I have known Barry for many years. On arrival, he always complains incessantly about the distance he has to drive to get here and the terrible condition of the roads but, he is a nice man and is very reliable, and comes, winter or summer, without fail. I usually make him lunch and always listen to the same story every time, about the bad roads and the bad weather.

When I phoned, my listening and agreeing with him seemed to encourage him to come, and he said he would arrive in his lorry the next day at eleven o'clock, or thereabouts. Before he put the phone down, he had another little grumble, and I listened.

When I finished my phone call, George the Head mouse appeared and politely asked, "Can I come up?"

I liked the voice of George, it sounded very pleasant and very proud. I waved him to come up, and he ran up the arm of the chair, sat on his hind legs, and immediately clapped three times, then said, "Yes."

This very special greeting was unexpected, and I looked at him in astonishment. He must have seen my facial expression, for he smiled and said, "I did that to thank you for everything last night. What you did helped not only Horatio Science, but all the lighthouse mouse. I would also like to thank you for keeping our secrets," he paused, then continued rather seriously, "I hope you will always keep our secrets."

I was quite taken aback by his action and his little speech and, for a moment, I didn't know what to say.

He added, "As you know, Brian the Explorer is safe now, and Horatio Science has settled in very nicely. We shall all be very busy for the next few days, so I don't think any mouse will visit. Will you be all right?"

I smiled at his polite inquiry. "Yes, I will always keep your secrets and, yes, I think I will be all right, thank you. Anyway, I must make you aware of the arrival tomorrow of Barry in his lorry. He is going to change my containers, so I will be busy working on fastening and securing things inside the empty containers, to stop them falling about and breaking on the return journey to the depot."

"OK," said George, and he ran down the arm of the chair, stopped, and turned around. "I shall tell all mouse to keep out of the way. Oh, and thanks again." Then he was off.

CHAPTER 12
Barry in His Lorry

Early next morning, I went outside the lighthouse and finished securing all the returning items inside my containers, and waited for Barry in his lorry. At about ten-thirty it started to rain, so I prepared my wet-weather gear and continued to wait for his arrival. It was just after eleven when I heard him bouncing along the bumpy track to the lighthouse. I donned my rain gear, went outside, and waved a welcoming, enthusiastic greeting. His response was one of despair at the rain, which was now becoming rather heavy. Barry was a rotund man with a full head of hair and a fine moustache and, this morning, was wearing a remarkably snazzy pair of braces. He jumped down from his cab and put on his waterproof jacket. I gave him my spare sou'wester; he stuck it firmly on his head and emitted a lot of mumbling and grumbling, then immediately commenced lifting the containers on and off his lorry with his crane.

It was an operation he had carried out many times before, so I left him to it and went indoors to begin making lunch.

The rain continued during the whole operation of lifting and dropping the containers on and off the lorry. From time to time, I opened the door to see the progress he was making and, again, heard the mumblings and grumblings.

On finishing his task, he quickly came inside and removed his waterproof jacket, revealing his red, white and blue snazzy braces. With a nod of his head, he returned my sou'wester.

Lunch was ready, and he automatically sat in the chair at the table opposite me and handed over yesterday's newspaper, and also a list of the container contents for me to sign.

During the meal, he talked as usual about his lorry and the problems he'd had with the motor and the hydraulic crane, and the difficulty of the drive to the lighthouse. Then, suddenly, his conversation changed and he asked me if I had recently had a problem with the light on the lighthouse. This was unusual; he'd never said anything like this before. I replied by telling him a fuse had blown and the emergency generator had started, and I had now repaired the fuse and all was back to normal. He seemed happy with this explanation, although I noticed he wrinkled his brow and twitched his moustache.

We had silence for a moment, then he whispered, "I heard something about it at the depot; they said the generator had started, and it wasn't a test run."

I gently answered, "Ah, well, all is right now."

Upon my reply, his moustache had a bigger twitch, indicating he knew something but wasn't telling me.

I made him a nice cup of tea and waited to see if he was going to say more, but he just hesitated, stalled, rose from the table, thanked me, donned his jacket, opened the outside door, remarked it had now stopped raining, walked to his lorry, climbed into his cab, started the engine, opened the window and shouted,

"Some time back along the road, a very large eagle started to follow me; it was a big one, you had better watch out," and he waved. I waved in return and watched him go bumping along down the track, then I turned and checked the containers and re-organised all the items.

It was quite late when I finally sat down to relax in my armchair. I couldn't get certain things he had said out of my head; why had he hesitated, stalled, and whispered when talking about the light going out in the lighthouse and the emergency generator starting? I pondered this, but my main thought was how far did the eagle follow Barry in his lorry?

CHAPTER 13
Daffodil

The following morning, I busied myself working hard on the lighthouse and, by ten o'clock, was ready to have my usual tea break. The previous evening, I had written a note on a piece of paper and placed it in my beautifully-carved message mouse.

It read, 'Please, could George the Head mouse come and see me at ten o'clock tomorrow morning?' On reflection, the message seemed a little stern and reminded me of similar ones I often received from my old school teacher. My sternness couldn't be helped, it was very important for me to see him. I had to be insistent. I knew he had received it and was coming, because the paper had been refolded and someone had written 'Yes' on it.

At precisely ten o'clock, George the Head mouse appeared in his usual colourful attire, only this time in different-coloured trainers.

"Hello", I said, "come and sit on the arm of my chair."

Without any hesitation, he quickly scuttled up the chair and sat down on his hind legs, put his head to one side, and asked. "You wanted to see me?"

Trying my best not to alarm him, I gently spoke in a calm voice. "Yes, I have some news for you, and I don't think you will like what I am about to say."

He looked at me, and his face took on a very serious expression.

I continued, "Yesterday, Barry came in his lorry."

"Yes, we saw him," he said, his face still serious.

"I'm sorry to tell you, an eagle followed him along the road, and it may just be possible this very large bird of prey might have followed him all the way here."

George didn't move a muscle or say anything, he just maintained his eyes staring at me, and was as silent as a mushroom.

We had a long pause, and I could tell he was thinking.

I didn't quite know what to do, so I waited and waited. Eventually, he slowly spoke, choosing his words carefully.

"First, thank you for letting us know and, second, for us Lighthouse mouse it is a very serious situation. If the eagle arrives here, it will sense our presence and, therefore, we must not, under any circumstances, go outside. What we must do is devise a way of making it go away and never return, but without harming it."

My immediate thought was that these mouse are not only highly intelligent, they are also extremely brave.

George looked at me with determination in his eyes. "I will ask Daffodil to come and see you. She is our tracker and observer mouse. She may need information. I will send her at fifteen hours. Is that all right?"

"Yes," I said, and he was off.

From what I had just witnessed, George regarded this possible intrusion as a very grave affair, and I saw it was my place to help the mouse in any way I could.

To stop me from worrying about my new friends and the danger the eagle would present to them, I took my spade on this very sunny day and worked hard attending the garden.

The flowers were beginning to bloom, and the vegetables were showing a fair amount of interest in the sunshine.

After I had returned to the lighthouse and had a quick lunch, Daffodil the tracker and observer mouse appeared. I couldn't help noticing, even on this serious occasion, how stylish her green trainers, green-striped breeches and green top were. I also noticed she had a bag strapped over her shoulder.

In a very fine, high-pitched voice of a young lady, she said, "Hello, I'm Daffodil," then she politely enquired if I had a map of the local area.

Before doing anything, I asked, "What's in the bag?"

She unbuttoned it, took out a pair of yellow binoculars, and placed them to her eyes. She smiled as she saw I recognised why she was called Daffodil.

A search of my shelves produced a large map of the local area, and the table provided a platform for it to be spread upon. She took my invitation, and very quickly came up onto the tabletop and walked across the map, looking at all the roads.

CHAPTER 14
Daffodil's Plan

I sat on a chair at the table with the map spread out in front of me and watched Daffodil the observer mouse, in her fashionable trainers, walk directly along the roads drawn on the map. I waited until she had surveyed enough to sufficiently discover her bearings. Her wandering took her from where the lighthouse was, then along the track where Barry had driven his lorry. Then on to the point where it joined a side road and onto the main road. She stopped at this junction, turned toward me, and pointed at a position on the map.

"After Barry arrives here in his lorry, which direction does he take?"

"He takes that road," and I indicated on the map the road leading straight on.

She stood thinking, then walked along it a few steps, saw it disappeared off the end of the map, and looked at me. "This road goes a long way."

"Yes," I said, "we are very remote out here."

She walked further along the road on the map, then strolled back, all the time thinking and pondering as she went. I looked on in wonderment as this gentle little creature assessed the situation with very great care.

She saw I was waiting, and smiled a very big smile. "Sorry I am taking so long, but I must get the most likely direction the eagle will take if, indeed, it decides to come our way. For us lighthouse mouse an eagle is a formidable assailant."

I waited. "Take as much time as you want; oh, and if I can help further in any way, you only need to ask."

She put her hand up to her chin. "Thank you; it looks highly likely we will require your help. But first, I must get Isambard the Designer mouse to draw some plans for an automaton mouse, then get Big Sam, Mabel, Ronnie-Odd-Socks, Marilyn and the team to set about making it. Finally, I will ask Horatio Science to mix some chemicals, and work together with the Cook Captain to make a substance strong enough for our purpose."

This was suddenly something very new to me. I couldn't understand why chemicals and cooking were needed to stop an eagle. Daffodil saw the inquisitive expression on my face, half-smiled, walked opposite to where I was sitting and sat on her hind legs. "I think I must hurry back and begin preparations. I would like to return tomorrow at the same time, but first I will ask Professor Universe to come and see you and explain things. If I need to change anything, I'll leave a message on message mouse. Is that OK?"

It all sounded a very good plan, although I didn't understand the finer details, so I just said, "Yes," and she scurried off at top speed.

I attended to things in the lighthouse, then went outside with my binoculars to search for this assailant. In the beginning, the sky was clear of any birds but, after I walked further past the vegetable plot and on toward the garden shed, I saw a speck in the sky. It wasn't long before a dark shadow fell across my path. It moved so swiftly, I found it difficult to follow and eventually lost it in the sunlight.

I very quickly came to the conclusion we definitely had a massive bird in our midst.

More searching of the sky found no further image of the eagle, and I returned to the lighthouse, now convinced the assailant was lurking somewhere out there.

CHAPTER 15
The Automaton

On my return to the lighthouse, I sat in my armchair thinking about the danger the eagle would present to the Lighthouse mouse, and came to the overwhelming conclusion it would be very dangerous indeed. As I was contemplating the situation, Professor Universe arrived and asked to come up onto the arm of my chair. I nodded for him to come, and he clambered up the leg and settled himself on the arm.

I greeted him. "Hello, Professor; I was informed you were coming."

He was soberly dressed and had quite a serious expression on his face. He spoke with a voice in between one of gentleness and one of authority.

"I have come to tell you that Daffodil has spotted the eagle in the vicinity, and it is a very dangerous situation indeed for us lighthouse mouse."

I listened, and waited for him to continue. He looked directly at me, his face thoughtful and earnest. "We must do something about the presence of this creature."

He shuffled a little in his seated position and prepared himself to speak at length. "As Lighthouse mouse, we must defend ourselves but, in so doing, we must try our best not to inflict injury on any of our own, or any other living creature, which includes the eagle. Its presence here creates a very delicate and very serious situation indeed, and we must show the utmost care. As you know, we are going to make an automaton mouse, and I have come to tell you it has already been designed by Isambard the Designer mouse, and is presently in the process of being constructed. Every single lighthouse mouse is involved in the manufacture of this extremely important defence machine. It is going to be a technical masterpiece with Isambard, Big Sam, Mabel, Horatio and Marilyn all working to their maximum ability."

As he said it, he raised himself, and I saw a profoundness appear; he maintained it, then he sat and waited for me to say something.

I didn't disappoint him. "That is the longest speech I have heard anyone say for a very long time, and I would also like to confirm the eagle to be in the vicinity. I have seen it circling over the vegetable plot and the garden shed today."

His face changed to one of thought and resourcefulness. "Yes, Daffodil saw it circling the garden shed and vegetable patch; it must have sensed our presence." He paused and looked down, as if in thought. "We do require your help and we need to know if the eagle will attack you."

This question had never crossed my mind, but thinking about it caused me a little concern. Fortunately, I wasn't a small man and thought that maybe the bigger I was, the safer I would be.

I replied with a question. "What do you want me to do exactly, Professor?"

"Ah, yes; when the automaton is completed, it will look and move about exactly like a mouse, but it needs to be positioned at the far end of the garden, where it can be seen by the eagle. The garden shed is a long way from the folly, and the terrain leading to it is rough, and the automaton mouse may struggle to get that far by itself and could possibly run out of energy. We need you to take it and put it down in the grass near the garden shed. It may be a very dangerous walk for you - by all accounts, the eagle is very big."

He was right; from what I had seen, the eagle was very big indeed, and I took a moment to think about what he had said.

CHAPTER 16
The Decision

I would have to walk a long way in the open to reach the shed at the far end of the garden. The eagle could easily spot if I was carrying anything like a mouse about my person; even if I hid it, the eagle would be able to sense I had it. The walk would be a very dangerous task to undertake. If I was attacked by the eagle and badly injured, the situation could become very grave indeed for me. This lighthouse is so remote, doctors, nurses and hospitals are such a long distance away and, with the very difficult roads, it would take a very long time to get medical treatment.

The situation was awkwardly challenging, so I asked the Professor a question. "Am I allowed to take something with which to defend myself?"

The Professor opened his eyes wide and considered what I had said, and replied, "Yes but, in so doing, you must try your utmost not to injure the eagle or yourself."

While pondering this thought, it suddenly occurred to me: how were the lighthouse mouse going to make the eagle go away permanently, but not injure it?

I asked the Professor the question.

His answer came in a very direct manner.

"The automaton mouse will look, feel, and smell exactly like a lighthouse mouse on the outside, but not on the inside. When the eagle sinks its claws into the automaton mouse, the substance inside created by Horatio Science and the Cook Captain will be released. The smell produced will be so horrible to the eagle that it will be able to fly only a certain distance and, eventually, it will be forced to drop it to the ground; then it will fly back from whence it came and never return."

He then produced a half-smile and whispered, "We know that, when the eagle punctures the body of the automaton with its claws, the smell will be too great for it to bear. It is very important to get the automaton mouse to the other side of the garden shed."

His half-smile and his reply were as stern and as serious as I had ever seen or heard from any lighthouse mouse.

It encouraged me to come forth with my reply; "I shall be honoured to take the automaton mouse to the far end of the garden for you, and place it on the other side of the garden shed."

Professor Universe looked directly at me, and I could see my answer was important for he radiated a huge smile, placed his hands apart, clapped three times, said, "Yes," then smiled the broadest smile I had ever seen.

"We will have the automaton mouse finished at 10 hours in the morning. Marilyn and the team will bring it here to you, inside the lighthouse. Presently, other than Marilyn and the team, all lighthouse mouse are on lockdown and are not allowed to venture outside under any circumstance."

"Yes, I understand the situation must be very dangerous for all the lighthouse mouse. I will be here waiting at 10 o'clock in the morning."

The Professor smiled a gentle smile, scrambled down the arm of the chair, waved smartly, and walked solemnly away.

I had much to do in the lighthouse, and time was moving very quickly.

CHAPTER 17
The Team

The following morning after completing my chores, I sat in my armchair and pondered over what the Professor had said. I couldn't help thinking how was it possible for Marilyn and the team to bring the Automaton mouse from the folly to inside the lighthouse without being seen? If they were to venture outside the folly, they must be very careful, or go with utmost speed.

Over the last weeks (or was it months?), these lighthouse mouse had created many mysteries for me and, so far, I had not been able to solve any of them. The biggest mystery, apart from their sudden arrival, was how Horatio Science had rapidly and unexpectedly appeared when I closed and opened the blind for the light to shine directly on the place where the main part of the river met the sea. The area of water for them at that particular spot must be like the area in the Atlantic Ocean called "The Bermuda Triangle," where very suspicious actions occur in very mysterious circumstances. It is a particular area in the world where a large number of aeroplanes and ships are said to have appeared and disappeared. I am very much aware of the lighthouse mouse suddenly appearing from nowhere, and am now getting quite used to it. But the sudden appearance of Horatio Science mouse on the lighthouse light platform, at the exact stroke of midnight, was an ultra-extraordinary happening.

I was thoughtfully speculating about the situation and thinking, if my attention were taken away, Marilyn and the team would arrive with the Automaton mouse. Sure enough, while I was pondering this, a noise somewhere drew my attention and I heard a female voice say, "Hello, Mr Lighthouse man."

I looked down, and there at my feet were Marilyn and the team, dressed in their colourful trainers, socks, breeches and waistcoats.

"Hello," I said, and remarked how smart they were. All the team waved to me and laid the Automaton mouse on the floor. Marilyn introduced me to everyone, which took rather a long time.

I looked at the Automaton mouse; it was the same as all the mouse except it wasn't dressed. Its coat was a smart grey and made of a smooth, brushed material, making it look exactly like a lighthouse mouse without their fashionable clothes and footwear.

The team stood back and Marilyn looked up at me. "We haven't put the auto in a bag or a sack, or anything like that, because it would take you too long to unload when you arrive at the other side of the garden shed, and we have made it appear like all other mouse, not like lighthouse mouse. Do you think you can carry it in your hand? The Prof informed us you are going to take something with you to defend yourself."

"Yes, I am proposing to take my automatic umbrella in one hand, then I can carry the automaton in the other."

Her face showed a question; "How does the automatic umbrella work?"

"Ah, yes; it has a button near the handle; when I press it, the umbrella opens automatically."

"Ah, that sounds like a very good defender indeed." She put her thumbs up, and the team showed signs of their approval.

I asked, "Can I lift the automaton to see how heavy it is?"

Marilyn and the team shuffled a little further back; I leaned forward and picked the automaton up with my left hand and felt it was a good weight.

"It is a nice weight!"

"Yes," she said, "it is the same weight as an ordinary mouse."

"Good; I shall easily be able to carry this and the umbrella to the garden shed." This brought forth a great deal of excited chatter from all of the team, and I placed the automaton back on the floor.

CHAPTER 18
The Journey

As I sat back in my chair, I noticed Ronnie-Odd-Socks had arrived. "Hello, Mr lighthouse man." He had a gentle voice, although one that encouraged you to pay attention.

"Hello, Ronnie-Odd-Socks; like your trainers."

"Thanks; thought I'd wear my best for this occasion," and he winked at me. "I've come to explain to you all about the automaton and how it works."

I sat back, made myself comfortable, and prepared myself to listen.

"First it is best if you don't drop it. Second, try not to squeeze it too hard and, third, to turn it on just press the nose."

He paused, saw I wasn't going to say anything, so continued.

"We will know when you switch it on, and we will begin to move it. When it is working, it moves exactly like a mouse and, to let you know we have control, we will walk it to the right, and then walk it to the left. Have you any questions?"

I looked at him and the team; they all peered at me with wide-open eyes. I suppose I could have asked many questions, like, how far could it walk and how bad was the smell, and others, but thought it more important just to carry out the instructions properly rather than make enquiries, so

I replied, "No, I think it is all very straightforward. When can I start on my journey?"

Ronnie-Odd-Socks smiled in acknowledgement of my keenness and proposed, "Right; as protection, I suggest you wear your heaviest coat with long sleeves, and put on leather gloves if you have any."

I had a sort of trench coat I rarely wore, because it was made of very thick fabric and rather heavy. I fetched it from the entrance hall, put it on, and buttoned it right up to the collar. A search in one of my drawers produced some leather gloves, and I slipped them over my fingers. Ronnie-Odd-Socks, Marilyn and the team watched everything with interest.

After taking in my hand my automatic umbrella from the stand, I then bent down to get the automaton. The trench coat was very thick and very stiff, and I struggled to get anywhere near bending to the floor and very nearly fell over. All the team moved out of the way to one side and said, "Oh," altogether.

Finally, I steadied myself and raised my eyebrows. "I think I am ready now; can the team lift the automaton up and lay it in the palm of my hand?"

Marilyn requested the team to do this, and they raised it above their heads. With a lot of effort, I crouched down, slipped my left hand under the automaton, settled it in my gloved hand and stood upright. I then tucked the umbrella under my left arm to free my right hand. All the mouse were now on their hind legs, their eyes fixed on me. "Right," I said, "I think I am ready," and I headed towards the door leading to outside.

Before I reached the door, Ronnie-Odd-Socks asked me to wait, and I turned around.

"Mr Lighthouse man, all the lighthouse mouse are aware you are making this very dangerous journey for us, and we are all very grateful. We all hope everything goes well and you place the mouse on the other side of the garden shed without any problem. I cannot explain how important this is for all of us, and we would like to show our appreciation."

There was a split second of silence, then they all raised themselves up on hind legs, moved their arms apart, clapped three times in unison and said, "Yes."

The whole thing brought a lump to my throat, and I struggled to reply but eventually managed to say, "I will do my very best," then I opened the lighthouse door and went outside.

CHAPTER 19
The Dark Shadow

Outside the lighthouse, the air was fresh and clear. I took the closed umbrella from under my left arm and gripped it firmly in my right hand in readiness to defend myself. With the automaton mouse held firmly in my left hand but not squeezing it, I stood upright and straight in preparation for whatever was before me. Looking far ahead into the distance, I could just see the shape of the garden shed, and figured it would take some time for me to get there, so I decided on this occasion to do a marching pace when walking.

First, I tramped along the gravel track, then joined the lengthy grass path between the vegetable patches. The sky in front of me was clear, and I was beginning to think the journey to the shed would go without incident, and I became more confident in my strides.

Suddenly, without any warning at all, a dark shadow appeared above me and blackened the sky. For a fleeting moment I thought a cloud had passed across the sun and temporally switched it off. I looked up and found I needed to shield my eyes with my arm, for they were caught in the bright sunlight. The sun blinded me momentarily and I lost my bearings. This made me stop in my tracks, which was probably the worst thing I could have done. I knew in that split second of time it wasn't a cloud passing in front of the sun, it was the dark shadow of the eagle as it swooped down with howling speed directly above my head. I ducked down slightly to avoid it and, from somewhere in me, I found the courage to continue marching along the path. I gripped my closed umbrella more firmly in my hand in readiness to protect myself, the thought being that, if the eagle had tried once to get the automaton mouse, it would definitely try again. By marching, I quickly arrived at the end of the flower beds.

Then suddenly, from nowhere, I saw the eagle approaching out of the sky at an extraordinary speed. It was now close enough for me to see the enormous wingspan and the outstretching, razor-sharp talons. The very quickness of the approach startled and frightened me so much that I inadvertently, although fortunately, pressed the button on my umbrella, and the canopy began to open. It was when the umbrella opened fully the eagle struck. The force of the strike was so violent it nearly tore the handle from my grip; the leather gloves saved the day, and my grip stayed firm. The eagle clawed and battled with so much ferocity and fierceness it tore holes in the canopy of the umbrella. Unfortunately, my concentration was so steadfastly fixed on what was happening in the sky, I momentarily let go of the automaton mouse and saw it was falling to the ground, luckily, I deftly caught it by the tail, and a catastrophe of enormous proportions was avoided.

I do not think the eagle liked the canopy of the umbrella, or the fabric it was made from, for it flapped its massive wings and took off at high speed. I maintained the bedraggled umbrella up in the air, which was a reminder to the eagle not to attack again, and made my way to the place behind the garden shed, hanging on to the automaton by its tail.

In the sudden silence, I could feel my heart beating very fast, and knew I had very little time to carry out my task so, as quickly as possible, I laid the automaton on the ground in the grass and pressed the nose. For a second there was no response, and I thought that by catching it by the tail I had broken it; then, suddenly, it moved to the right and then to the left. I breathed a sigh of relief and allowed myself a satisfied smile. The job I came to do was done.

I turned away and began quickly walking back to the safety of the lighthouse. With each step I felt relieved and, by the time I reached the end of the vegetable patch, my heart was beating only fast, which was an improvement on very fast. Keeping the umbrella up in the air all the way to the lighthouse seemed to be important, and I was very pleased to see the entrance door. It was a great relief to open it, enter the lighthouse, and shut the door behind me. I stood for a moment inside with the umbrella still up in the air, then remembered it was unlucky to have an umbrella up inside the house; but, in this instance, I didn't mind. I looked at it and thought that it wouldn't be any use at all now in the rain, as it was in complete tatters.

CHAPTER 20
The Unexpected

I stood with the broken and ripped umbrella in hand, wondering what on earth to do with it. Eventually, after a struggle, I managed to close it and walk over to the corner of the room and stand it upright. I took off my heavy trench coat and hung it on the peg; removing my leather gloves made me think how useful they were on my journey to the garden shed, remembering they had saved the day more than once.

I needed a drink quite badly and, after boiling the kettle, I made a mug of tea, carried it to my armchair and, with a great deal of pleasure, sat down. I began pondering over what had happened on my journey to and from the garden shed, and thought how lucky I was not to sustain any injury.

After I finished my tea, I must have slipped nicely into an exhausted sleep, for I woke with the empty cup in the crook of my finger and a lady mouse on the arm of my chair.

She saw me wake and said, "Hello, Mr Lighthouse man; I am Mabel the Assistant Engineer mouse. I hope you don't mind me sitting here." She was dressed in pink breeches, with a brown waistcoat and brown trainers, and looked very pretty.

I blinked and smiled; "No, I don't; it's nice to see you."

She had a very broad grin on her face and spoke very politely. "You were successful in your journey to the shed, and I am very pleased to say the eagle took the bait and grabbed the automaton mouse. Daffodil, our observer mouse, with her Super Binoculars, was able to see the eagle flying high above the path heading in the direction of the main road with the mouse in its talons. They must have cut into the body of the automaton because we are aware, because of the dreadful smell, it released it and dropped it to the ground after some distance. The substance won't do any harm to the eagle, only make it smell for a bit. It dropped it in an area where there are few creatures and, because of the smell, they will keep away. The automaton mouse will take time to dissolve, but will eventually become compost and produce extra green grass in the ground."

I was delighted and said, "Well, Mabel, I'm very pleased to hear the plan worked; it must now be much more comfortable for all the lighthouse mouse."

"Yes, it is, and, because of it, we are all having a celebration tomorrow afternoon at fourteen hours. You are invited. Will you come?"

"Yes, of course; I will be delighted to come."

She then ran down the side of the chair, turned at the bottom, stopped, and shouted, "Good. Lucinda Lids will come for you," and she was off.

The rest of the day went very quickly and I slept very well indeed after my scary adventures.

The following day I donned my best clothes; it was a shame I didn't possess any brightly-coloured trainers, thinking I may be the odd one out with my ordinary black shoes.

I was settled in my armchair reading a book after lunch when Lucinda Lids appeared, and boy, was she dressed for a celebration. The eyelashes were bigger than usual, and the socks and trainers were pink. She had on the usual breeches, but the waistcoat was covered in many different-coloured flowers. She was really prepared for a celebration.

"Can I come on to the arm of the chair?" she asked.

It was impossible for me not to smile and shake my head from side to side. "Yes, of course you can, and you look spectacular."

She ran up the arm of the chair, lifted her eyelashes, curtsied, then responded to my words in a voice with extraordinary pleasure and gentleness:

"Thank you. I have come to collect you and tell you it is time for us to go and join in our celebration of singing and dancing. We are assembling in the covered veranda, built all those years ago outside the folly." She looked at me. "I see you are ready."

"Yes, I am looking forward to it. I'm sorry I have no trainers."

She ran down the chair and, when I stood to walk to the door, she was gone.

I was getting used to this appearance and disappearance, and now rather took it for granted.

CHAPTER 21
The Celebration

The weather outside the lighthouse was glorious, and the long walk was a pleasure. I made my way around to the other side of the folly and saw Lucinda Lids waiting for me at the back of the covered veranda, sitting on top of the old stone table. In front of her on the floor was a multitude of mouse, all decked out in gloriously-coloured breeches, waistcoats and trainers.

Lucinda Lids invited me to sit on one of the chairs next to the table. As I sat down and looked up, all the assembled mouse turned to me, clapped in unison three times, and said, "Yes."

I don't know quite why I did it but, for some reason, I naturally responded by clapping three times myself and saying, "Yes."

This little effort on my part brought a great cheer from all of the mouse assembled.

When things settled down and quietness prevailed, George the Head mouse stepped forward, looked up at me, and arranged himself to make a speech.

"Mr Lighthouse man, all the lighthouse mouse would like to thank you for the bravery and tenacity you showed in helping us persuade the eagle to fly to another place and never to return."

At this point, there were a few calls of "bravo, bravo!" He smiled, waited, and then continued; "During yesterday and today, not only have we all been preparing for this celebration, we have been making a special token of our gratitude for you, Mr Lighthouse man."

He stopped speaking, and allowed Marilyn and two of the team to enter, carrying what was, to them, a very large, square piece of shining metal.

George began speaking again. "We would be honoured if you would accept this gift as a reminder of what you did for us lighthouse mouse, and we hope you will wear it, at all times, from now on."

I was astounded at what had just occurred and suddenly became very emotional. Nothing like this had ever happened to me before, and I struggled to hold back a tear of disbelief and gratitude combined.

George spoke up, "Can you please take the gold medal from the team? It has a clip on the back for you to pin to your chest."

I bent down and gently lifted the medal out of the hands of the two mouse. The bottom of the medal was engraved with the words, 'Mr Lighthouse man' and, above it, was engraved a drawing of the broken, tattered umbrella. It was just perfect. I raised myself high above the mouse and pinned it to my shirt. As I did this, the whole of the lighthouse mouse clapped three times in unison and then shouted, "Yes!"

Lucinda Lids lifted her hand and put it to her heart, and indicated for me to do the same. I did exactly as she did, and she smiled a most radiant smile.

Music started from a small band, and all the mouse began to dance. I watched in wonderment as they all danced in the same way, all in unison, graciously stepping and swaying to the music. It was a wonderful sight to see.

I saw George the Head mouse dancing and caught his eye, indicating for him to come up onto the table. He came, and I said to him, "I would like to make a speech to thank everyone."

He smiled, turned to the lighthouse mouse, and held his hands in the air. Slowly the music stopped, and there was a lovely quietness. George turned to me and bowed gracefully, inviting me to speak.

From my sitting position, I looked over all the assembled mouse. "Thank you all very much for this beautiful medal; I think the inscription and the design are wonderful, and I will cherish it forever. I would also like to thank you for your friendship and your camaraderie. It was an honour for me to help you." I then clapped three times and said, "Yes."

It wasn't the same as when the lighthouse mouse did it, but I enjoyed doing it, and they all smiled. The music started, and the dancing began again.

I informed George I must return to the lighthouse. I said goodbye, and left all the mouse beautifully dancing, singing and celebrating.

CHAPTER 22
Bartholemew and Gilbert

The following day, a written message appeared on my message mouse. It read, 'Daffodil will arrive at fourteen hours.' I wrote 'OK,' and returned it to the mouse. It was a good time for me because, by then, everything in the lighthouse looked clean, shipshape and ready.

I was dozing when she arrived and was woken by her soft voice calling, "Mr Lighthouse man." Daffodil was beautifully dressed as usual in her green waistcoat, with the bag containing her yellow binoculars slung over her shoulder.

I greeted her; "Hello, Daffodil; how are you?"

"Very well, thank you, and fully recovered from the celebrations. I've come to tell you I watched the eagle yesterday until it was out of sight. Unfortunately, I didn't see it drop the automaton. It would be good if we knew where it was."

She paused after saying that, and stared at me with a worried look on her face. "Can I come up and sit on the arm of your chair?"

I nodded, which was all that was necessary, for she came up, settled down, looked straight at me, and spoke rather seriously.

"To replace Brian the Explorer mouse, we have two up-and-coming explorers, Bartholemew the Explorer mouse, and Gilbert the Explorer mouse and, much to everyone's disapproval, they set off this morning in search of the automaton mouse. We all think it is too dangerous for them to go out at the moment, but they said they are very good friends, and they will be all right and will look after each other. We understand they want to prove themselves worthy explorers, and that this is a good opportunity for them to do so. Also, it will be very good if we can recover the automaton, so no one else will find it, if you see what I mean."

My face was one of deep concern. "Yes, I see what you mean - if someone finds it, they will wonder where it came from and come searching, which is exactly what we don't want." I contemplated the situation for a moment then asked, "I haven't met Bartholemew or Gilbert; are they young mouse?"

Daffodil breathed a sigh; "Yes, that's the problem; they are very young mouse, but they were so determined to go, to prove themselves to be good explorer mouse. In the end, everyone waved them off. They promised to be very careful."

I could see she was concerned about their safety. "Do you think they will be all right?"

"Well, they have taken with them, in their backpacks, extra energy accumulators, and other pieces of equipment which were possibly damaged on the automaton when it fell to the ground. If they find the automaton, they can attach the new pieces of equipment to it. These will be sufficient to make it walk again and only stop when it returns to the position on the other side of the garden shed, where you placed it."

She stopped speaking for a second. It gave me the opportunity to ask, "What about the smell?"

"Ah, yes, Bartholemew and Gilbert have the equipment to enable them to reduce the smell considerably, but they will still have to block their noses. All lighthouse mouse have a very strong sense of smell, and the odour from the automaton when it is breached will be excessive - they will have to be very careful. Eventually, to remove the smell from the automaton, Marilyn and four of the team will take a Do-da-cover and place it over the automaton to eliminate the smell completely. The Do-da-cover has handles so it can be carried easily by the team."

I wondered what a Do-da-cover was, decided not to ask, but did respond by saying, "Will you be watching the progress of Bartholemew and Gilbert on their exploration?"

"Yes, I have a tracker on them, and every lighthouse mouse is hoping they will be all right."

I asked, "Can you please let me know when they arrive back safely and if they find the Automaton?"

"Yes, I will return later this afternoon." She then curtsied, ran down the arm of the chair and was off.

CHAPTER 23
View from the Pocket

It was in the early evening when Daffodil reappeared. I could see a tear in her eye and immediately said, "Come and sit on the arm of my chair."

She slowly made her way up to the arm, and I saw tears running down her little cheeks. "Tell me what has happened, Daffodil."

In the beginning, she couldn't speak for the tears. I waited, and waited, very concerned and worried. Eventually, she gathered herself together and, with some difficulty, began speaking.

"It is now nightfall, and we haven't seen or heard from Bartholemew or Gilbert for a long time. We know they have replaced parts and attached the homing device to the automaton, and we also know it arrived at the garden shed some time ago. Bartholemew and Gilbert should be home by now, but they aren't. We have had no communication from them for hours and hours."

She pulled a little tissue from her binocular bag and wiped the tears away. With Brian the Explorer leaving to go to Mouseland recently, and now the two boys missing, this was a serious and very upsetting situation indeed for the lighthouse mouse. I could see they needed help, but what was I to do?

My lighthouse light was on because it was dark, but it faced out to sea, which was the wrong way to search the land. I knew I had to think of something to help the lighthouse mouse. Suddenly I had an idea. Inside the store next to the lighthouse was a powerful, portable light, to be used only in an emergency if all else failed with the lighthouse light. I thought this was definitely an emergency and suggested to Daffodil we take it along to the garden shed and use it to search for the two boys.

As an afterthought, I added. "Daffodil, it is very dangerous for you outside; it is best you make your way back to the folly. I shall go by myself."

Her reply was instant; "No, I want to stay and help you. I have my powerful binoculars with me, I will be able to see a great distance."

She said it in a really persuasive manner, forcing me to reassess the situation. On hearing the determination in her voice, I gave in. "Well, Daffodil, we must be very careful. I will wear my heavy trench coat for the journey, and you can ride along with me to the shed in the side pocket. What do you say?"

With renewed vigour, she wiped her eyes. "Yes, I would like that."

I took my coat off the peg and put it on, fastening it tight. "Now, Daffodil, I'm going to lift you up and put you into my left-hand side pocket. Are you ready?"

"Yes," came the reply.

I bent down, and she jumped onto my hand. As I lifted her and placed her in the pocket, this gentle little creature called out, "Weeeeeeee." We needed something to cheer us and encourage us along, and this was it. It made me smile.

"Are you comfortable in there?"

"Yes, I am, and I can see out; it's quite good up here." Doing something instead of just waiting and watching had inspired her.

"Right, I'm going to walk to the store and get the portable light and take it to the garden shed, then place the light facing up the track that leads to the main road."

"OK," she said.

Outside was very dark, but the lighthouse light shining brightly on the sea just allowed me to see my way to the store. I went inside, took hold of the battery-powered portable light, and lifted it up by the carrying rope. I went back outside and walked the distance to the garden shed with Daffodil as lookout in my pocket.

On our arrival, we found the automaton or, rather, smelled it.

Daffodil looked up at me and said, "It's lost a lot of its smell; I'm sure it was a lot worse when it was first breached. Can you please put me down onto the ground?"

I lifted her out of the pocket onto the ground. She went over to the automaton, took something out of her binocular bag, pointed it at the automaton and sprayed a substance on it.

"That will get rid of a little more of the smell. Will you be able to carry the automaton back to the store on our return to the lighthouse? The team can collect it from there."

I looked at her in the dark. "Yes, I'm sure I can," and I walked across to it. She was right; the smell wasn't nearly as bad now. I placed the automaton on top of the portable light and tied it down using part of the carrying rope. I then switched the portable light on and placed it into a position where it shone its light directly down the track, and we both looked after it. Daffodil asked if she could return to the pocket, I lifted her, and she snuggled down inside, took out her binoculars, and put them to her eyes.

With concern in her voice, she enquired, "Can you see the two boys anywhere?"

"No, I can't see any sign of them, and a mist has now descended to make it extra difficult."

CHAPTER 24
The Darkness

We both tried to look through the mist to see if we could see any sign of Bartholemew and Gilbert, but there was nothing.

Daffodil looked up at me from the pocket. "Mr Lighthouse man, can you turn please so I am facing directly up the track?"

I did as she asked. "How's that?"

"Yes," she said, "that's a lot better."

I looked with my eyes, and Daffodil looked with her binoculars. The mist was making it even more difficult to see up the track. Suddenly, Daffodil whispered, "That's better; I have switched my binoculars over to anti-fog."

I was yet again surprised by the technology possessed by these lighthouse mouse. They had binoculars able to see through the mist and fog; it was incredible.

We both stood and stared along the shaft of light for what seemed an age. The longer we looked, the more concerned I became, and was on the point of thinking we would never find them. The mist was thickening, making it even more difficult for me to see; my eyes were straining and I had to keep blinking.

After what seemed a long time, the voice from my pocket said, "Hello; I'm sure I've seen a movement up at the far end of the track. Can we walk up the track a little? I'm sure there is something or someone up there."

My immediate thought was, let's hope it is something or someone friendly. I picked up the portable light and walked slowly along the track. The voice came again; "Yes, there is definitely a movement coming this way; it is following the path of our light."

Daffodil suddenly let out a shriek, and I'm sure everyone for miles would have heard it. Then she excitedly shouted, "Yes! It's the boys! I recognise their waistcoats; they are moving very slowly, but we are getting nearer to them all the time." The excitement in her voice was now at fever pitch.

As we got closer, she became more excited and started jumping up and down in my pocket. "Yes!" she shouted, "It's the boys!"

She took her binoculars down from her eyes and sadly said, "Oh, no, Mr Lighthouse man, one of them is injured; that's why they are going so slowly."

I could now see faint movement coming towards us down the track, and one of them was limping badly.

Daffodil looked up at me. "Gilbert has injured himself. Can you lift me and put me down on the ground so I can greet them?" I gently took hold of her and placed her down onto the track.

She immediately scurried off up the track to them and put her arms around them both. Then she and Bartholemew helped Gilbert along as best they could. I met them and turned to Daffodil.

"I've got a plan, Daffodil. Can I put you and Gilbert into each of my side pockets? But first, can I tuck Bartholemew into the front lapel of my coat? If we do that, we will be able to get to the lighthouse much quicker."

She agreed and said, "That's a great idea, Mr lighthouse man," and I saw a faint smile appear on her face.

I thought it best for me to give some instructions. "Right, Bartholemew, I'm going to lift you and put you up inside the lapel of my coat. When you are securely in there, you must hang on, because I am going to bend down and lift Daffodil and Gilbert, and place one in my left pocket and the other in my right pocket. Right, are you all ready?"

I heard shouts of "Yes!" Even Gilbert managed to raise his voice and say yes.

CHAPTER 25
The Walk

The mist was getting thicker, but I could still make out the three little figures on the ground. I bent down and saw Bartholemew with his arms in the air, waiting for me. I gently lifted him with my right hand and placed him between the lapels in the crook of my coat, pulling them out slightly with my left hand to fit him in. Fortunately, he was the right way round, but he still shuffled himself about until he was facing outwards properly, then he put his arms outside to get a better grip of things.

I asked, "Are you comfortable in there, Bartholemew? And can you take a tight hold, because I am going to bend down?"

"Yes," came the reply, "I can see out, and I am hanging on to the lapels of your coat."

"Right," I said, "I'm going to lift Daffodil and Gilbert both together and put one in each pocket." It was then I noticed a splint and bandage tied on Gilbert's right leg and, as I lifted them both, I heard Gilbert yell in pain. I put them both back down onto the ground and changed my mind. "I can't do both together - I will do one at a time. First, I will lift you, Daffodil, then Gilbert."

"OK," she said, and she prepared herself like Bartholemew and raised her arms. I lifted her with my left hand and placed her in the right-hand pocket. I told her to grip my coat and heard her say, "OK," again.

I then turned my attention to Gilbert, and I could see by the expression on his face that he was in pain, but also his expression indicated he was trying his best to be very brave.

"Right, Gilbert," and, as I spoke, I saw him put his arms in the air like the others. My heart went out to this gallant, adventurous lighthouse mouse; he was undoubtedly doing his best. I bent down and, as gently as I could, took hold of him with my right hand. Then, with my left hand, I ever so slightly opened the left-hand pocket of my coat and placed him inside, facing out.

"Grip the coat," I whispered to him. He winced, but did as I requested and looked up at me. His eyes were fully open, and I could see from the expression on his face that he was not looking forward to the ride back to the lighthouse. Hopefully, it was going to be quicker and less painful for him than limping along if he walked.

I bent and picked up the portable light with the automaton tied to it and, as smoothly as I could, began the journey back to the lighthouse. I found if I kind of slithered my feet along when walking, like a soldier slow-marching, it gave me less up and down movement. Whenever my footsteps did anything other than slither, there were little yelps of pain from Gilbert.

Using the portable light to see my way, and watching the ground in a determined effort not to stumble, eventually the travelling mouse transporter arrived at the lighthouse. I switched the portable light off and left it by the side of the lighthouse door, for Marilyn and the team to later remove the automaton using the Do-da-cover.

I opened the front door of the lighthouse, went inside, stood in the centre of the room, looked at my three companions nestled in various parts of my coat, and thought that I must now somehow get them all down onto the floor.

It wasn't going to be easy; a plan was best. "Right," I said, "I shall lift Gilbert down first," and I opened the pocket he was in. He looked directly at me with eyes wide open, and put his arms in the air, and I lifted him to the ground. In the light, it was plain to see his clothes were covered in dirt and grime, and his trainers and socks were unrecognisable. The bandage around his leg had loosened and was about to fall off. The poor mouse was definitely in a bad way and needed help quickly.

CHAPTER 26
Gilbert and Bartholemew

I looked at Gilbert and decided it best for him to sit down. The only thing I could think of for him to sit on was a book, so I removed a very thick history book from the shelf and put it on the floor. Gilbert sat on it and said thank you. The other two observed all this with interest from where they were. Bartholemew turned his head and looked up at me as if to say, "Is it my turn next?" I nodded my head.

"Are you ready, Bartholemew?" Without saying anything, he put his arms in the air; I lifted him from the lapels of my coat and put him down onto the floor. He wasn't as dirty as Gilbert, but his trainers and socks were covered in grime. As soon as I let go of him, he ran straight to his pal and carefully hugged and hugged him. They then spoke very quickly to each other; so quickly, I was unable to understand what they were saying.

I saw Daffodil, in the other pocket, put her arms in the air, wanting me to lift her down. I took hold of her and gently lifted her to the floor; she joined the other two hugging, and more hugging, and then united in the same excitable chatter.

While this was going on, I took the opportunity to remove my coat and, with great pleasure, sat down in my armchair. I watched the three lighthouse mouse together in heavy conversation, incapable of understanding a word they said. They saw I was looking at them and stopped what they were doing. All three then turned to me, sat in a line on my book, waited, settled, paused, then clapped three times in unison, and said, "Yes."

For me, it meant all the thanks in the world, and put a smile of extraordinary proportions on my face.

Bartholemew spoke up. "We must go back to the folly and let Doctor Dexamethasone fix Gilbert's leg; plus, we all need to get cleaned up and changed. I think you realise we have shown gratitude for what you have done, but we need to go now."

They both joined their arms together behind Gilbert to support him, and they moved across the room. I bent down to pick up the book and, in that instant, they were gone.

My lighthouse was functioning properly, and my light was bright, enabling me that night to go to bed in peaceful satisfaction.

My alarm clock woke me the following morning, and I took a few minutes to lie and rest in bed, pondering over the previous evening's adventure, particularly lingering on hoping Gilbert was going to recover from his injuries.

Before attending to the lighthouse, it was necessary for me to clean the very important portable light and return it to the store.

During morning tea, my mind was occupied thinking about the very quick chatter the mouse made, when they were hugging each other, and the different language they spoke. My thoughts were disturbed when I noticed a piece of paper in my message mouse. It read 'H.M.G. B.G. D.D. will arrive at fourteen hours, hope it is OK.'

I didn't immediately understand what H.M.G. B.G. D.D. meant, but still replied, 'OK'.

CHAPTER 27
Doctor Dex

I sat for a while and worked out what the message stood for, and figured it was, 'Head Mouse George, Bartholemew, Gilbert, and Doctor Dexamethasone will arrive at fourteen hours.'

At precisely fourteen hours, all four mouse appeared, and I went over, sat in my armchair and greeted them. Before they said a word, they stood in a straight line and, in total unison, clapped three times and chorused, "Yes!"

I would never get tired of this obvious thank-you, and I smiled a big smile. All mouse before me were dressed in their Sunday-best clothes, all with the same-coloured breeches and socks, but with different coloured waistcoats and the usual, highly-coloured individual trainers.

Gilbert had a kind of plastic tube covering the full length of his injured leg, and was using a pair of crutches to support himself and yet, somehow, he had managed to clap his hands in unison with the others. On his feet, he had succeeded in fitting a pair of new, highly-coloured trainers.

George the Head Lighthouse mouse thanked me for what I had done the previous day and introduced me to Doctor Dex. He was quite young-looking and wore black-rimmed spectacles; also, I noted he shortened his name to Doctor Dex. I was intrigued by the plastic-like tube on Gilbert's leg and asked him about it. He explained how the broken leg had now been joined together, and a substance specially manufactured by the lighthouse mouse moulded over it. He then went on to say, "The tube will be left in place for a few days and monitored from inside. When the electronic information received indicates that the leg is healed enough, the tube will be removed, and the leg will be as good as new."

He finished speaking and saw my wrinkled brow. "Yes, you are thinking that, if humans had this substance and the relevant information and technology, it would make life a lot easier." He paused; "There are a lot of other things you could benefit from us," and he paused again, looked at me as doctors do, and said, "But we are happy how it is."

It would take an awful lot of thought to figure out what that meant, and I left it for a later date.

George scratched the back of his head in such a way as to say, "I think the doc has said enough," and quickly came forward. "Thank you for what you did, Mr Lighthouse man; we are now all going to have a mouse party," and they all walked across the room. As I looked at my watch for the time, they were gone.

The following morning, I received a rare and upsetting telephone call from the depot. Arnold, the new whizz-kid technical engineer rang in a very confident voice and said he was coming to see me the following day at about 10 o'clock, and had a new and improved electronic panel and was going to make the lighthouse totally and fully automatic.

This lighthouse was the last lighthouse in the country to have a lighthouse man, and he said the big noise in the depot would very much prefer this lighthouse to be automatic. They had tried in the past and not succeeded, but it sounded this time as if they were quite determined. It meant only one thing - they were trying to operate the light without me living here.

The possibility of not being here in the lighthouse upset me. This lighthouse was my life, and my life was even better now because these lighthouse mouse were all my friends. I loved them, and they loved me, and I loved my life as it is.

I sat in my armchair and wondered why they couldn't make this lighthouse automatic the last time they tried. Did it have something to do with the lighthouse mouse? I needed help, and put a long message in my message mouse. It read, 'Depot trying for automatic tomorrow, help wanted, please, please come at fourteen hours.'

To stop myself from worrying, I went to my vegetable plot and worked as hard as I could. It improved the garden, but it didn't stop me worrying and thinking about what was going to happen.

Eventually, I thought, "Think positively;" maybe, the lighthouse mouse could do something.

I really, really hoped this wasn't the end of

Mr lighthouse Man and the Ingenious Mice.